Violin
Scales &
Arpeggios from 2012

Why practise scales?

Welcome to this book of scales and arpeggios for Grade 1 Violin. Practising scales and arpeggios plays an essential part in developing a player's skills. Time devoted to these exercises within each practice session will improve many aspects of technique, such as co-ordination, string crossing, bow control, position changes and tone production. In addition, the sense of key and pattern acquired through familiarity with scales and arpeggios has several benefits: it speeds up the learning of new pieces, builds aural awareness, increases familiarity with the geography of the instrument, and helps develop fine intonation, evenness of line and quality of tone.

For the exam

Tempo
The candidate should aim for a tempo that achieves vitality of rhythm, controlled bowing, good intonation, and a clean, sonorous tone. Slurred patterns should generally be played with the whole bow, while separately-bowed examples should be played with a smooth *détaché*, using no more than half the bow length.

The given metronome marks indicate suggested *minimum* speeds for the exam. Candidates may feel that slurred requirements become more comfortable when played at a brisker tempo than examples with separate bows, such differences in speed being dependent on factors such as size of instrument and length of bow. Experienced teachers will know what their candidates are able to achieve safely, although it is important to avoid accurate yet laboured playing which demonstrates that the pattern has been memorized but lacks the musical fluency needed for a convincing result.

Fingering
Any practical fingering that produces a good result will be accepted in the exam. The decision as to which fingering to adopt will vary between players, taking into account ease of performance, memorability, and the importance of changing position unobtrusively, and candidates should experiment to find solutions that work for them. (Examiners will not comment on the choice of fingering, unless it interferes with the musical outcome of the performance.)

On the day
All requirements must be played from memory. Examiners will usually ask for at least one of each type of scale or arpeggio required at the grade, and will aim to hear a balance of separately-bowed and slurred requirements.

The examiner will be looking for:
- good intonation across the pitch range
- an even and positive sense of rhythm
- accurate and fluent realization of the different types of scales and arpeggios
- confident, controlled, and consistent tone
- convincing negotiation of technical challenges such as string crossing, position changing, and co-ordination.

Rhythm patterns

For major and minor scales candidates may choose between two rhythm patterns: even notes *or* long tonic.

In this book, major and minor scales are presented in even notes first, followed by the same scales using the long-tonic pattern.

Published by ABRSM (Publishing) Ltd, a wholly owned subsidiary of ABRSM

Reference must always be made to the syllabus for the year in which the exam is to be taken, in case any changes have been made to the requirements.

GRADE 1
SCALES even notes *or* long tonic at candidate's choice

EVEN NOTES
separate bows *and* slurred

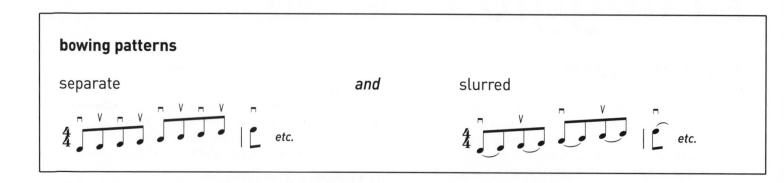

one octave ♩ = 52

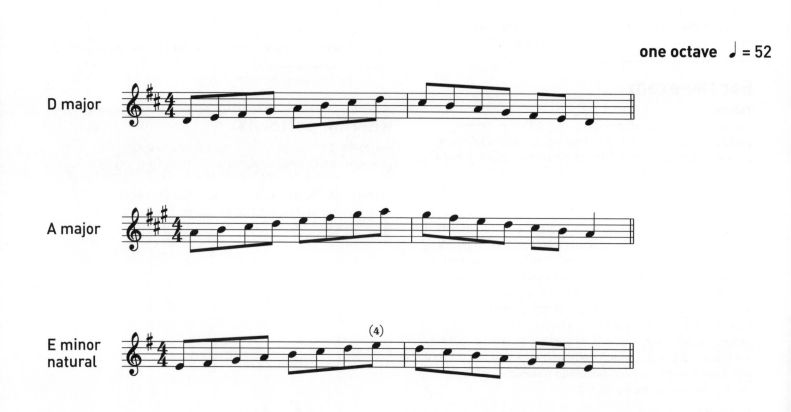

two octaves ♩ = 52

AB 3588

LONG TONIC
separate bows *and* slurred

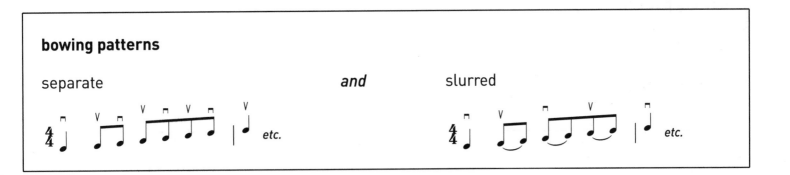

one octave ♩ = 52

D major

A major

E minor
natural

two octaves ♩ = 52

G major

ARPEGGIOS

separate bows only

bowing pattern

separate

etc.

one octave ♪ = 104

D major

A major

E minor

(4)

two octaves ♪ = 104

G major

Music origination by Julia Bovee

Printed in England by Caligraving Ltd, Thetford, Norfolk

AB 3588

09/11

Violin Exam Pieces

ABRSM Grade 1

Selected from the 2012–2015 syllabus

Piano accompaniment

Contents

Violin consultant: Philippa Bunting
Footnotes: Edward Huws Jones (EHJ) and Anthony Burton

The pieces in this album have been taken from a variety of different sources. Where appropriate, they have been checked with original source material and edited to help the player when preparing for performance. The fingering and bowing have been amended where necessary to ensure a consistent approach within the album. Ornament realizations have been added, as have metronome marks shown within square brackets. Details of other editorial amendments or suggestions are given in the footnotes. Fingering, bowing and all editorial additions are for guidance only; they are not comprehensive or obligatory.

ABRSM Violin Exams: requirements

Pieces
In the exam, candidates must play three pieces, one chosen from each of the three syllabus lists (A, B and C). Candidates are free to choose from the pieces printed in this album and/or from the other pieces set for the grade: a full list is given in the violin part with this score as well as in the 2012–2015 Violin syllabus.

Scales and arpeggios (see 2012–2015 Violin syllabus)

Sight-reading (see 2012–2015 Violin syllabus)

Aural tests (see 2012–2015 Violin syllabus)

First published in 2011 by ABRSM (Publishing) Ltd, a wholly owned subsidiary of ABRSM, 24 Portland Place, London W1B 1LU, United Kingdom

© 2011 by The Associated Board of the Royal Schools of Music

Music origination by Andrew Jones
Cover by Økvik Design
Printed in England by Halstan & Co. Ltd, Amersham, Bucks.

Mattachins

Arranged by Edward Huws Jones

Thoinot Arbeau

A 'mattachins' is a sword dance that was popular in Europe from the 16th century to the 18th. The tune included here first appeared in print in Arbeau's *Orchésographie* (1588), alongside pictures showing how the dance should be performed. The tune was given a new lease of life when Peter Warlock included it in his *Capriol Suite* (1926). The sword-dancing origins suggest how it should be played: it needs to be lively and boisterous! EHJ

Menuet

from *Music for the Royal Fireworks*, HWV 351

G. F. Handel

Arranged by Lionel Salter

A:2

George Frideric Handel (1685–1759) was born in Germany, but spent the last 47 years of his life in England, where he became famous as a composer of operas, oratorios and instrumental music. In 1749, he wrote his *Music for the Royal Fireworks* to accompany a fireworks display in Green Park in London celebrating the end of a European war. It was played by a band of about 100 musicians: oboes, bassoons, horns, trumpets and drums, and probably strings as well, in defiance of King George II's reported remark that 'he hoped there would be no fiddles'. The music consists of a large-scale overture followed by a series of dance movements, of which this joyful minuet is the last.

A:3

German Dance

from K. 605 No. 3

Arranged by Mary Cohen

W. A. Mozart

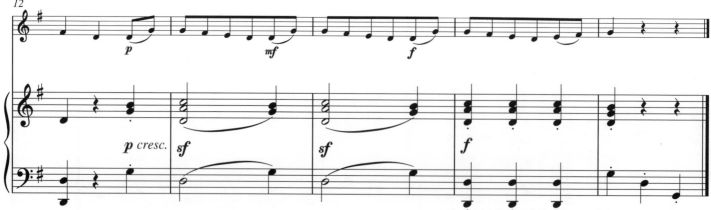

The Austrian composer Wolfgang Amadeus Mozart (1756–91) wrote operas, symphonies, concertos and many other major works, but also numerous sets of dances – many of them, in the later part of his life, in fulfilment of his duties as 'chamber musician' to the Austro-Hungarian Emperor at the court in Vienna. This German Dance (a forerunner of the waltz) comes from a set of three for orchestra which Mozart wrote in February 1791 for a carnival dance in Vienna. Its middle section or trio, not included in this arrangement, is the well-known *Die Schlittenfahrt* (Sleigh Ride) with five jingling sleigh bells.

Sandmännchen

No. 4 from *Volks-Kinderlieder*, WoO 31

B:1

Arranged by Lionel Salter

Johannes Brahms

Sandmännchen Little Sandman; **Volks-Kinderlieder** Folksongs for Children

The German composer Johannes Brahms (1833–97), famous for his symphonies and concertos, had a strong interest in folk music, and published several collections of arrangements of German folksongs. The first of these, which appeared in 1858, was a set of *Volks-Kinderlieder*, dedicated to the young children of his mentors Robert and Clara Schumann. It includes 'Sandmännchen', a song about the mythical Sandman who lulls children to sleep and brings them pleasant dreams by sprinkling magic sand into their eyes. This arrangement preserves not only the melody of the song but also Brahms's piano part, although it shortens the original postlude.

The Boat to Inverie

Edward Huws Jones

The Scottish village of Inverie is one of the most isolated communities on the British mainland. The only access to it is by boat or a 20-mile walk across the hills. EHJ

Edward Huws Jones (born 1948) is a well-known composer and arranger, with a wide-ranging knowledge of fiddle playing styles around the world and a special interest in music for young string players. He has acted as consultant and editor for ABRSM on numerous projects. *The Boat to Inverie*, in the style of a Scottish folksong, is from his *Violin Star* series.

Daisy Bell

Arranged by Mark Mumford

Harry Dacre

The English songwriter Harry Dacre (1860–1922) had his biggest hit in 1892 with his waltz-time song *Daisy Bell*, a favourite in the music halls of both London and New York. It remained popular for many years, and in 1961 became the first song ever sung by a computer. This arrangement presents just the chorus, to the words:

> Daisy, Daisy, give me your answer, do,
> I'm half crazy all for the love of you.
> It won't be a stylish marriage –
> I can't afford a carriage,
> But you'll look sweet, on the seat
> Of a bicycle built for two.

Pennsylvania 6-5000

C:1

Jerry Gray
and Carl Sigman

Jerry Gray (1915–76) was an American composer and arranger of the big band era, well known for his work with the bandleaders Artie Shaw and Glenn Miller. It was for the Glenn Miller Orchestra in 1940 that Gray, in collaboration with Carl Sigman (1909–2000), wrote *Pennsylvania 6-5000* – named after the telephone number of the Hotel Pennsylvania in New York, where the Orchestra was appearing at the Café Rouge Ballroom. This arrangement comes from the collection *What Jazz 'n' Blues Can I Play?*, edited by Mark Mumford and Tim Siddall. The editors suggest unhurried swung quavers (as indicated above), slightly shortened crotchets in bar 2 and similar bars and 'some crescendo for expressive effect within phrases'.

C:2

Russia – Gopak

No. 5 from *Travel Tunes*

Margery Dawe

'Margery Dawe' – the pseudonym (writing name) of a music teacher in south-east London, who died in 2001 – composed and arranged many books of educational music for piano, recorder and various string instruments. This piece comes from a collection of six *Travel Tunes* for violin or viola or cello and piano, published in the 1950s. It is in the style of the gopak (or hopak), the energetic national dance of Ukraine, which is now an independent country but was formerly part of the Russian Empire and then the Soviet Union.

© 1957 by J. B. Cramer & Co. Ltd

Reproduced by permission of Cramer Music Ltd. All enquiries about this piece, apart from those directly relating to the exams, should be addressed to Cramer Music, 23 Garrick Street, London WC2E 9RY.

C:3

Dvoják

Couple Dance

Arranged by Leoš Faltus

Leoš Janáček

Leoš Janáček (1854–1928) was born in a village in Moravia, in the eastern part of the present-day Czech Republic, and lived for many years in the Moravian capital, Brno. He was an enthusiastic collector of the folksongs and dances of his native region, which influenced the melodies and rhythms of his operas and other music, and which he also published in his own arrangements. This is a version for violin and piano of Janáček's sketch for a piano arrangement of a couple dance from the Haná region, in alternating pairs of bars of 2/4 and 3/4 with the crotchet beat constant.

Violin Scales & Arpeggios

This new edition contains all the scales and arpeggios required for ABRSM's Grade 1 Violin exam.

Key features:

- all scales and arpeggios for the revised syllabus from 2012, with bowing patterns
- helpful introduction including advice on preparing for the exam
- user-friendly format and clear page layout

A selection of support material for ABRSM Violin exams

ABRSM's mission is to motivate musical achievement. We aim to support the development of learners and teachers in music education worldwide and to celebrate their achievements. We do this through authoritative and internationally recognized assessments, publications and professional development support for teachers, and through charitable donations.

ABRSM
24 Portland Place
London W1B 1LU
United Kingdom

www.abrsm.org

ISBN 978-1-84849-338-4

Oxford University Press is the sole worldwide sales agent and distributor for ABRSM Publishing.

A workbook for examinations
Including over 100 practice tests for Associated Board exams
Supports syllabus requirements from 2009

Grade 3
Piano

Improve your sight-reading!

Paul Harris

Faber ƒƒ MUSIC